Big Tom

Written by
Stephen Rickard

Illustrated by
Andy Hamilton

Ransom

Big Tom can tuck a sock
in his back pack.

2

Big Tom can tuck a ticket
in his top.

Big Tom can tuck a duck
in a bucket.

Big Tom can kick a rock
into a gap in a sack.

Big Tom can pack an egg
in his bag.

Big Tom can get a bug
off his mug.

But Tom can not get a rocket
in his pocket!